INSP

An anthology of artwork, memoirs, poetry, and short stories

QUILLKEEPERS PRESS

ISBN:979-8-3596-4172-2

Dear Reader,

If someone else's work has never moved you to the point you needed to write or create a piece of art inspired by the original, are you even a writer or artist? We've found that most creatives love and thrive in creating fanfiction, and our editors and publishers are here to support it.

Fanfic is a popular genre, but that is not to say it doesn't come with a mountain of stigma and restraints. If one is not careful, one can get into trouble for copyright infringement. Therefore, it is always important to double and triple-check the subject matter and how you are going about creating your fanfiction.

In putting this anthology together, we hesitated for the reasons mentioned above. We had to abide by a strict screening process during our selection process. We were overwhelmed by the outpour and sheer volume of submissions we received. We were equally devastated that some submissions did not fit the guidelines and criteria we sought. For those that made it into this anthology, thank you. We appreciate your contributions more than we can express.

Short Stories

Mieke Leenders 11

Our Cosmic Ties 12

Aysel K. Basci 27

Maneuver 28

Kimberly McAfee 35

The Cuatro Killer 36

Cheryl Walsh 45

Haarlem Proposition 46

Anthony Samuels 51

Cosmic Showers 52

Khadijah Danielian 57

Fireside 58

Memoir

Dan R. Tardona 69

Stirred by Seafaring Art and Poetry in Brooklyn 70

Poetry

T.C. Anderson   **75**

Space Cowboy   76

A Promise Kept to a People Who Forgot What It Felt Like to Fly   78

Stephanie Lamb   **79**

Portia's Gold   80

Winter is Coming   81

Tin Man   82

Superman   84

Mark Andrew Heathcote   **85**

Almond Blossoms the Deferring Sentence   86

Orlando   87

The Artist's Restorative   88

Dana Trick   **91**

A Poem About Guts from Berserk   92

Utena   93

Anthy   95

Button-Eye Witch   97

Would You Kindly . . .   98

Enoch Black   **101**

Why I Love Dragons   102

Sleeping Dragon   104

Dragon Songs   105

What Is a Group of Dragons Called?   106

Bruce Parker   **107**

  The Hunt   108

  Aleatoric Ode to Alexander Liberman (1912 - 1999)   110

  James Abbott McNeill Whistler (1834 - 1902), Lady Mieux (1881)   111

  William Merritt Chase (1849-1916) Did You Speak to Me?, about 1897   112

  Gelatin Print on Paper   113

Roger Camp   **117**

  The Cisco Kid   118

  Art History's Splashy Smear   119

Kimberly McAfee   **121**

  Sorry, Sorry: Forever Love   122

  The Silver Smartphone   123

Karin Eaton   **125**

  Into The Abyss   126

  A Humble Salute to Amanda Gorman   127

  Rainbow Tunnel (Light at the End of the Tunnel.)   128

  Reflections On a Wall   129

Daniel Moreschi   **131**

  Solar Swansong   132

T.M. Thomson   **133**

  Fig Mother   134

  Rumors of Spring   135

  Reflection   137

  Grazing   139

  Maria Sibylla Merian, 17th Century Artist & Naturalist, as Goddess   141

Phyllis Castelli   **143**

   Peace   144

Suzanne Cottrell   **147**

   What's the Rush?   148

Original Artwork

Jenny McKinnon Wright   **153**

   What's the Rush   155

Mieke Leenders is a freelance writer and published author with a master's degree in Art History and certificates in Teaching, Journalism, and Editing. Her writing is published or forthcoming in *The Abstract Elephant Magazine, The Bluebird Word,* and *The Write Launch.* Originally from Belgium, she set out on a solo backpacking trip in 2017, which led her to put down temporary roots in Costa Rica. Mieke is passionate about nature, travel, hiking, literature, photography, animal welfare, social justice, and art.

Our Cosmic Ties

By Mieke Leenders
Inspired by Van Gogh and Jean-Francios Millet

My Dearest Theo,

There have been very few times the voices guiding
me were just my own. You used to say I am an idle
bird. That I have started and ended more careers
than the sky has breaths. And yet, I began all of
these because you told me to. Or because father did.
Painting finally felt like something of my own. But
even here, I used to be guided by others more so
than myself. The Parisian salons. Fellow artists. My
precious Millet... I remember when I first saw The
Sower. The simple farmer who possesses an air of
true nobility that only Gods and royalty had earned
before Millet reset our gaze.

Jean Francois Millet, The Sower, 1850

Vincent closed his eyes as he tried to summon one of his most treasured visual memories.

Striding with powerful legs that could rival Michelangelo's Hercules. The Hero of the Common Lands. Closest to nature. Closest to death.

Walt Whitman once described this painting as having a sublime murkiness, Vincent recalled.

Smile, O voluptuous cool-breath'd earth!

He clutched the poetry collection resting in his lap while he followed the patterns shaping the morose serenity of a barren field.

Millet's earth was not smiling. Nor was it voluptuous.

It screams. It wears the same face as the sower who, despite his heroics, was, in turn, mirrored in these hungry soils.

Vincent remembered his earlier years as a painter when his own observations of peasant life lacked any hint of a more soulful intuition. *Provence is no place for murkiness, however sublime. It 'should' yield an earth that is voluptuous. And the peasants that populate them, should still be as real, as grotesque, as expressive as the colors that reflect our innermost selves.*

Do you remember my second portrait of Escalier, brother? Do you remember his shoulders hunched over his walking stick? The color, burning, scorched, with the blistering heat of orange and yellow hues? That's who he was. So, this is how I painted him. The salons of Paris prefer to be told about life through sentimental doodles. Reality… 'my' reality, seems to act more like a repellent. Millet made them uncomfortable too. Still, Millet and I paint a different reality.

His fingertips drew closer, pausing right before they could make contact with the canvas.

We all create. We sow ideas. Sometimes before they are ready to grow.

Like an ugliness that unsettles. A reality more genuine than truth.

Millet was not wrong.
Just further away.

Vincent looked up from his paper at a room that only answered in darkness. While the memory of his most recent crisis was a haze, these last few weeks have felt like he was living inside a portrait someone else had painted of him. Some stranger, who had never met him before sat down, picked up a brush resting on a monochrome palette, and absentmindedly composed a few crude features. He had started to put himself back together, but the disturbing portrait had left its mark. *A mark that can't be painted over, however bright my own palette.*

I am further away as well. Even from where I was in Arles not too long ago. However much I cherish them, my farmers, Millet's farmers, they all feel like they belong in a different life. I rarely pursue my passion for portraits anymore. Not that I have much occasion to. Even now, when thinking about dear Millet who had always been something of a balm, the comfort is temporary. The inspiration fleeting. The connection, somehow, disjointed.

The last portrait I painted was one of a fellow traveler with a mind and a face as ancient as the gnarled trees in the asylum gardens. Not ancient like a prophet, but ancient like a drifter forced to live the lives of countless unwelcome ghosts. Do you remember the portrait, brother? I admit it wasn't my finest hour from an artistic perspective, but I asked this man to sit for me for one reason only: his eyes. That is where the ghosts still live. The director insisted none of the other residents sat for me again after that, as if I had revealed some horrible secret.

Vincent van Gogh, Portrait of a Patient in Saint-Paul Hospital, 1889

He sat back, thinking that despite this isolation, he did welcome that rare silence so hard to come by within these walls. The daily torment knowing that anytime chaos could break loose. More than a couple of times, that chaos was caused by his most recent subject.

I do still see portraits everywhere, even if I don't feel as inclined to paint them. These faces, every little blemish, wrinkle and twitch tell a story. Every narrative as beautiful and haunting as the next. And as true. Each of our stories are set in the same hollow world. All we really do here is bury ourselves deeper into our own minds because of this curse that has been cast on us: time. Time spent alone. Time spent in reflection. At least I still have my art. My books.

Well, I don't have my art right now. Although I do have one book.

This little book was the most precious item in the world right now. Vincent placed his hands on the thin, worn copy so delicately as if any impulsive movement would turn it to dust. As his fingertips moved across the torn edges, he reflected on the words that have shaped him into the artist who's sitting on this chair right now.

Emile Zola's gritty truths.

Charles Dickens' passionate morals.

Victor Hugo's portraits of human depravity.

George Eliot's odes to country life, ...

Walt Whitman's visual poetry mapping our soul.

The sun was setting over the gilded wheat fields, beaming with light as if God himself had painted them. Vincent longed to be outside and explore the vibrant patchwork of olive groves and vineyards just beyond the town center. The cicada will be taking the stage soon, with the coming season laying out a warm bed for him. A warmth that turns the air thick and moist, alive with more scents than a fresh food market.

Only in the Provence, is your sweat seasoned with the zesty richness of rosemary and thyme. And only here, are the nights void of a cutting blackness, and instead, speak of a promise.

He smiled.

I suppose I have come to appreciate nature itself as a portrait.

I have been rediscovering my love for the poetry collection by Walt Whitman. It is one of the only objects I have had in the room for these past few weeks other than some paper and chalk. I don't know if it is the book itself or the fact that it is the one piece of literature I have been reading (and re-reading) for such a long time, but Whitman's words have been both terrifying and delighting me.

In some ways, Whitman puts into words what
Millet puts onto canvases. The inherent nobility of
the common man. But, while Millet's farmers reign
over little more than their crops, Whitman moves on
to take us on a vision quest. This is where I connect
most with his words. Where he celebrates the
unparalleled expressiveness of nature. Something I
have been feeling more in touch with since coming
here.

Every step I take out into the countryside feels like
my first steps into a new life. And with every step, I
feel these hills are wanting me to slow down.
Tempting me to walk and ponder, to paint fields that
transform with every passing cloud. Mere patches
of land engineered feed us, are lifted to something
prophetic and holy out here.

Night was close. Black trees towered over the dimly lit horizon like cloaked
guardians. The winds rocked their crown and their heads tilted, like a nod,
begging him over. He wanted to join them. Desperately. He longed for a friend
as precious and pure.

With the next gust of wind, their bodies seemed to grow, arching over the
slumbering town, watching like a curious visitor. There was nobody outside,
but some homes were still lit. A tiny speck of brightness that broke the trees'
dark figures with an orange hue forming near the roots. The winds jerked and

pulled, and for a moment, it looked like their roots were a prison. And that even comfort, nourishment, life itself, was worth escaping.

Nature is more than a collection of organisms. It is coming home. "Something fierce and terrible in me eligible to burst forth", Whitman observed in this earth of ours. I know this feeling very well. The sacred and the destructive. The innocence and the wild.

Yes... Innocent and wild. And there is nothing more innocent and wilder than trees. I wish I had my Wheat Field with Cypresses in here with me.

The sky, always moving, always changing.

And the blue. The pure, bright, blue set off by the cypress.

Its dark, scaled leaves moving upwards, like waves, towards infinity.

Do you remember the Wheat Field and Cypresses
I sent to you, brother? The director felt some
concern when he saw that one. A sky as erratic as
an ocean, he said. And the looming presence of
the tree of death.

Death. Yes. But more so the tree of durability and transition, surely. Vincent
thought. *Noah even built his ark with it. They guide. Sustain. Support.
Transport?*

Nature is more than what we see before us. We
are formed by it. Born from it. Whitman
understands this. He transcends the limitations of
our diseased minds and conquers both life and
death by reminding us of our cosmic ties. When I
read how he describes a world so balanced and
blooming under a sky gleaming with light, I feel
every inch of me coming alive with an almost
unbearable sharpness.

*That is what painting nature feels like... It is where we are born. Where we
delight. And where we return. It is the architecture of our body. It is the
blueprint for our minds.*

*I remember painting my Olive Trees with Yellow Sky so well. The yellow
lines pulsating, expanding, rhythmically, like a heartbeat. I wanted the
canvas to feel even hotter than the actual sun. I wanted the shadows to look
like melting tree barks spilling out over the grass.*

Liquid, like blood.

Vincent van Gogh, Olive Trees with Yellow Sky and Sun, 1889

I am reminded of how painting is an exploration of ourselves, in our bodies as well as our minds. You may remember my Olive Trees with Yellow Sky. Imagine the mountains that make up our mind, the sun that feeds it, the fields, our skin, the grass, our veins... The trees, our very foundation.

Iron bars cut the moon's naked skin. The cracked bone, brittle and aging, couldn't find any light, and so the trees were silent. On the opposite end of the horizon, a silent neighbor flickered gently. A whisper. It was unclouded and bright, like a mind in its infancy, exuding a peace that Vincent envied.

It is late. I can see the Morning Star. Even through barred windows, I am not blind to the brilliance of the only star with the heritage of a human heart. This cage used to compromise my view, but the bars have evolved into something more familiar, and a sight I welcome with varying degrees of enthusiasm. Sometimes, it embraces me with arms cold as night that gradually warm through our mutual touch. Other times, it greets me with a softness that stays with me all day, like a kiss on my skin.

Tomorrow I am getting my materials back and I can finally paint again. Released from this creative purgatory. Tomorrow, I paint. Tomorrow, I return to myself. And I return myself to the world. Is it a kinder world yet, Theo? How will it receive me?

Oh well, who can say what tomorrow will bring. Tomorrow is still centuries away. For now, Tomorrow is nothing more than a Utopian Dream.

Vincent van Gogh, Starry Night, 1889

'Our Cosmic Ties' first appeared in the Abstract Elephant Magazine Issue No. 2: Ideologies, Belief Systems, & The Human Condition, in December, 2020.

Aysel K. Basci, is a nonfiction writer and literary translator. She was born and raised in Cyprus and moved to the United States in 1975. Aysel, is retired and resides in the Washington, DC, area. Her writing and translations have appeared, or are forthcoming, in the *Columbia Journal, Los Angeles Review, Michigan Quarterly Review, Aster(ix) Journal, Critical Read, Adelaide Literary Magazine, Bosphorus Review of Books,* and elsewhere.

The Fisherman of Halicarnassus is the pen name used by Turkish author and intellectual Cevat Şakir Kabaağaçlı (1886-1973). An Oxford-educated historian, humanist, ecologist, and ethnographer who produced a variety of travelogues. Today, he is better known as a naturalist. His poetics of marine life, flora, and fauna specific to the Bodrum peninsula qualify The Fisherman as an important bioregional writer. Throughout his life, he worked tirelessly for marine conservation in and around Bodrum and helped establish top-quality ecotourism facilities in that region. He was a prolific writer. When he died in 1973, he left behind many novels, collections of short stories, and essays.

Maneuver

Translated by: Aysel K. Basci

Inspired by The Fisherman of Halicarnassus

Overnight, ten to fifteen fishing boats surrounded a deserted island in the open seas with their fishing nets. At dawn, as the fishermen's songs reached for the skies, they applied their strength to their oars, gathering their nets.

Normally their songs melted away sweetly into the blue sky. However, that day, they fizzled at their lips. An uneasiness hung in the air; even their hearts were gloomy.

An old fisherman said, "The seagulls are not flying over the boats today. Look! They are returning to their nests. This is not a good sign at all."

A strange silence enveloped them. Everyone kept a close eye on the weather. It was obvious the silent sea was expecting a storm. The fishermen scanned the horizon, wondering where the storm would erupt.

Their nets were full of horse mackerel, red bass, picarel, and haddock. Their holds were already half full with the wiggling silvery fish.

The Martı's captain, Yavaşoğlu, said, "Let's hurry up friends!" He was frowning.

Loud rumbles in the southeast sounded like fingers tapping on a drum. The fishermen, concerned about both their lives and their livelihood, gathered the nets as quickly as they could.

Soon, a vicious rustling emerged as if the boats' ropes were screaming.

From boat to boat, the captains cried out, "Cut the nets!" The knives came out, and the fishermen cut the nets as if cutting their own bloodlines. The

28

nets represented all that some of these poor fishermen owned as they slowly sank into the raging sea along with the red, blue, and green fish still trapped within them. By now, even the pulleys of the sails were snarling. The short storm sails were hauled in, slapping against the water when they busted free. In these unforgiving seas, hauling the red storm sails could only mean one thing: a life-or-death fight.

The first icy raindrops raced down to the sea, scaring the living daylights out of the fishermen as the winds ravaged the sails, whipped at the fishermen's clothes, and nearly ripped every hair from their heads. The fishing boats—now scampering from the hurricane as fast as they could—resembled women with long upturned skirts blowing toward their heads on a windy day.

When caught in the path of a hurricane generated by the emperor of the south, the mighty Provezza, the only option is to go toward it—ensuring either life or death.

At that moment, each boat had more than enough to do to survive, and their crews were trying hard not to let the boats get separated from one another. The incessant downpour was filling the holds with rainwater, and the crews were desperate in their attempts to empty them using any bucket they could find. The weight of the fish loaded in the boats pulled them low into the water, causing seawater from the churning waves around them to accumulate in the boats as well.

Soon the wind and rain were punctuated with shouts to throw the fish into the sea. Both fish and fishing nets were tossed into the sea. The downpour continued like giant gyroscopes swirling in circles, first gobbling up water from the sea and then spitting it out like useless rags, as they passed with the thunderous sounds of a thousand express trains.

Yavaşoğlu's Martı was considered a cursed boat. Since being built, it had capsized three or four times, and nine of its crew had died. There was something wrong with its structure. Although nobody could figure out exactly what its defect was, it was clear that the boat was fickle. If Yavaşoğlu turned the wheel even by a hair too much or took his eyes off the course for just a second, it would surely be the end of all those on board. Even now, for a second, the Martı's stern was down while its wheel was up in the air.

The boat immediately gave its sideboard to the wave. Yavaşoğlu ground his teeth so hard that he almost broke them. He was fighting both the storm and the boat.

Yavaşoğlu's son, fourteen-year-old Mehmet, squatted at the base of the pole used for the boat's safety line. He was holding the end of the line tightly in his hands, ready to either let go or pull in as soon as he heard his father's command. His eyes remained fixed on his father at the wheel, who would give the all-important command that would either kill them or save them.

His father yelled, "Let go!"

Mehmet let the line go. The boat's sail swung just above his father's head. A gigantic wave on their back pushed the stern high in the air. For a moment, Mehmet thought his father was flying in the air, with the bottom of the wheel still clenched in his hands. But the wave barked as it passed from under the boat.

The boy screamed "Father!" as his father sank deep into the sea along with the stern. But Yavaşoğlu was suddenly tossed up to dizzying heights. The Martı kept on flying.

Between the shrieks of the storm, human cries could be heard. Some of the men had already drowned. Foam and water bubbled up from the sea while also pouring from the sky. The Martı moved through a dark and chaotic nightmare. The clouds were like dungeons cracking over their heads, emitting layers of fire streaking through the skies. A sudden deluge rolled the boat twice before spewing the Martı into the air.

Yavaşoğlu, dared and sputtering from near suffocation, surfaced. He surveyed the scene. Two men were clinging tightly to the boat, but where was the third? Yavaşoğlu feared for his son, but asking about his son first was beneath his captain's dignity. So he asked, "Are you there?" using each of his crew's names. Finally, he asked, "Are you there, my son, Mehmet?"

"I am here!" Mehmet answered.

Yavaşoğlu shouted, "Hold on to the boat—all of you—as tightly as you can!"

In weather like this, the most likely outcome is death. However, the crew held on to the boat with their hands, fingers, nails, and teeth—whatever they could! To live one more second, they had to hold on one more second. Like animals feeling the pain of the knife sliding deep into their hearts during slaughter, they screamed for help. Their teeth chattered, and their eyes were blinded by the burning sea salt.

The dark sky was ripped apart by a huge bolt of lightning, and they saw a boat coming toward them. They screamed with pain, "Save us!"

The Umit was approaching, with Captain Habip, at the wheel. But then the Umit jumped about 20 meters ahead of them, its crew turning as they passed the Martı by to look at those they were leaving behind to the mercy of a dismal fate. They screamed with sadness. Trying to save those in the sea meant drowning and dying themselves—before saving them. They were apologizing to the friends they were abandoning.

From a distance, a human voice sounded. Another lightning bolt lit up the sky, and they saw the Denizkuşu coming toward them. Captain Ateşoğlu, who had fished with Yavaşoğlu for more than 30 years and had spent many good as well as bad times with him, was at the wheel. His eyes were full of tears. Ateşoğlu was going to attempt to do what the others could not. He commanded, "Round in!" He turned the wheel. The Denizkuşu turned to face a huge wave. Rounding in on such a treacherous day like this was foolish. However, Ateşoğlu was at the helm and was going to do everything he could. He turned the Denizkuşu around to look for the Martı. Lightning flashed, revealing the Martı in the distance. The Denizkuşu raced toward the Martı, but getting too close meant shattering the other boat into pieces. The Denizkuşu passed by the Martı. Ateşoğlu shouted through his megaphone: "Hang on, friends. We will be back!"

With perfect maneuvering, like a gyroscope spinning on its axis, he guided the Denizkuşu around. It lifted as high as the eye of the storm as it turned downwind. The Martı was not in sight. With the next flash of lightning, the crew on the bow pointed and yelled, "They are there!"

Ateşoğlu barked out his order. "Two men to the starboard and two to the port. Open your eyes really well! We can't repeat this maneuver many times." He continued: "One man stand next to the safety pole. When I say 'lower the sails,' do it fast!"

The Denizkuşu moved toward the Martı like an arrow shot from a bow. Each time the wind hit, the whole armada crackled like the bones of imprisoned men being tortured to death. When they were five meters from the Martı, Ateşoğlu screamed, "Lower the sails!" The Martı crested a huge wave.

Just as the wave was about to fall, Ateşoğlu yelled, "Hoist the sails!" The boat's yard was tossed in the air. Reaching into the sky, the sails were nearly shredded. Like a racehorse being whipped, the Denizkuşu took off, nose up, flying over the Martı from its side against the wave as Ateşoğlu yelled, "Take them in!" The crew reached out, over the railings and down to their waists, to pull their friends, grabbing their arms, hair, and chins—anything they could get a hold of. They swept them aboard as if emptying their daily catch of fish into the depository. Like swallows circling over a pool of water, pausing to quickly gulp in the water while still in flight, the Denizkuşu had plucked four men from the sea.

Ateşoğlu asked, "How many?"

The crew responded, "Three."

The Martı's captain said, "We are all here."

There was no time to exchange pleasantries. With its red sails, the Denizkuşu dove into the darkness and disappeared.

Kimberly McAfee, is a writer and poet residing in the US. She has authored/co-authored works in a variety of formats, such as websites, e-magazines, anthologies, and even a peer-reviewed scholarly journal. Ms. McAfee has also self-published three chapbooks available on Amazon. She is currently working on her first full-length poetry collection. You can find more of her poetry on her Instagram page @writerpoetkim.

The Cuatro Killer

By Kimberly McAfee

Inspired by the 1998 film, Dark City

Cold. Dark. Dank. Cobwebs hung from the ceiling like silvery lace that shimmered when illuminated by the flashlight.

"What a fucking shithole," Detective Pace said to himself. The smell of mold, urine, and feces filled his nostrils.

A series of murders rocked the city, Port Murdoch, and held everyone prisoner in their own homes. There was no modus operandi that could be determined among the victims: men and women of varying ages, ethnicities, and socioeconomic backgrounds…all were chosen at random; everyone was fair game to this killer. All were killed differently, too…something very unusual.

Some were shot, stabbed, dismembered, and some were beaten prior to death. Other than cruelty, the only connecting thread was the number 4; it was always written in blood next to the body. The local PD, the state investigative agencies, nor the FBI could figure out its symbolism. The media, in all their sensationalized ridiculousness, dubbed him "The Cuatro Killer."

Pace made his way through the hallway into the main room of the abandoned wax museum. Scenes of pop culture history lay in various stages of disarray: a figure that appeared to have once been Marilyn Monroe was demolished, with most of the body crushed into flesh-colored chunks of wax…the distinguishing wig and her tattered "The Seven Year Itch" dress lay alongside the pitiful sight. Elvis could only be identified from the "Jailhouse Rock" background. All that was left of the wax figure was an arm and the torso.

"All hail the King," whispered Pace. One must keep their humor in such situations.

The walls were covered in graffiti, and litter of all kinds covered the floor like a blanket of debauchery: needles, liquor bottles, beer cans, cigarette butts, tiny empty plastic bags, and other nefarious flotsam and jetsam.

This was once a thriving museum, but in the last several decades had fallen into disrepair along with the surrounding neighborhood.

The last murder occurred several buildings over; Pace and a few other Detectives were canvassing the area.

Pace had chosen this street, the wax museum being his final building to check.

CRUNCH, CRUNCH, CRUNCH. With every step, he crushed trash under his feet.

He inspected each area he came upon with his flashlight. More broken wax figures, more "Devil's trash," ripped pieces of clothing…possibly from the figures, possibly from some unfortunate soul who wandered into this forsaken place. This place could really be Hell, Pace thought to himself.

CRUNCH, CRUNCH, CRUNCH.

Pace thought of the other detectives, were they finished looking over their areas? He figured he would have heard something by now...if they had indeed found anything.

This group of detectives were the elite; they were the ones that had double-digit years of experience and were hardened by this life. But like Pace, they were all getting older. Retirement was on the horizon; some were looking forward to it, some weren't, but Pace was ready. There were too many dark things he had seen. He knew the depths of human depravity. Those are things that grate on a human being; the weight of such knowledge is nearly unbearable. He had no wife, no children. Pace just could not justify bringing new life into this world, let alone feel deserving of love. He had just been too close to the dark for too long.

CRUNCH, CRUNCH, CRUNCH.

"Stop," he muttered to himself. He really didn't need to be thinking about all this right now. There was a job, an incredibly important job, to do.

But Pace just couldn't stop himself from thinking about everything: his life, the choices he made. In times past, it was only during the sleepless nights that these sad thoughts would creep in. However, now with retirement coming, they intruded into his mind constantly.

There was no more repressing them now.

CRUNCH, CRUNCH, CRUNCH.

He was nearly done. There was nothing but trash, nothing but filth. No clues, no signs of a murdering fiend, just trash. Pace's mind began to wander again; he started to think of how he'd write about this field trip through the "Museum of Repulsive Waste" in his report.

That's when he saw it.

A bright white piece of paper neatly pinned to the back wall covered in indiscriminate smears, graffiti, and peeling paint; it was the only sense of normalcy, of cleanliness, in the whole entire dump.

Dear Port Murdoch Police Department,

Hello! I suppose correspondence is overdue. There have been so many stories about me in the news that I feel I've been neglectful in keeping to myself. Sincerest apologies! I do like the name I've been given--The Cuatro Killer--it has a nice ring to it. I must say, I have particularly enjoyed reading about your theories of motivation.

Oh, what fun! Satanism, Mommy issues, Daddy issues, countless potential mental illnesses, blah, blah, blah.

Why must there be reasons? Does everything need a reason? Why does he kill across genders, ages, and socioeconomic groups?

Why are some of the murders violent, but others appear methodical? What caused him to become this monster of a man? What does "4" mean?

You're all stupid! Every one of you! I have watched you all so many times, toiling away at the crime scenes like bumbling idiots, like fat stupid hippos...bumping into each other, talking your drabble of asinine theories. You all didn't even know I was there.

Why must there always be a reason? Nothing needs a reason! How delicious it is to be me! I indulge every thought that comes into my mind. I sink my teeth into every dark desire that manifests from the deepest recesses of my soul. I need no reasons! I take every moment of my life and choke every sweet drop of rage from it. Do you want to know who I really am? I am Death, the Destroyer of Worlds.

Every life I take is a world in and of itself...and I turn them to dust. What does "4" mean? Did I suffer a tragedy at that age, during that year of school, etc., etc.?

It has to MEAN something?!?!

Doesn't it? DOESN'T IT?!?!?

Oh, how delicious it is to be me!

I will tell you what it means. I will finally satiate your strange dependence upon knowing, upon understanding. That makes it all better right? If you UNDERSTAND?!?!? That way, it all makes sense. Oh, the sweet comfort sense brings. You are all such logical creatures, aren't you? You babes, needing the swaddling from the blanket of understanding. How pathetic you are!

Oh, how disappointed you're about to be.

*Oh, how **DELICIOUS** it is to be me!!!*

What does it mean? No more suspense! WHAT DOES IT MEAN?!?!

Nothing. It means nothing. It was a random thought that happened to manifest in my mind, that just so happened to be a number, that just so happened to be "4."

NOTHING!!! Oh, chaos, my favorite friend! Chaos is constant. Reasons mean nothing. Logic means nothing. Chaos fuels me. It births every dark thought in my mind, and I birth those thoughts into reality. I swim in the ocean of chaos and drink its sweet nectar.

My apologies. No comfort for you is to be had. 4.

4.

4.

*444444444444444444444444444444444444444444444
444444444444444444444444444444444444444444444
444444444444444444444444444444444444444444444
444444444444444444444444444444444444444444444
444444444444444444444444444444444444444444444
444444444444444444444444444444444444444444444
444444444444444444444444444444444444444444444
444444444444444444444444444444444444444444444
444444444444444444444444444444444444444444444
444444444444444444444444444444444444444444444
444444444444444444444444444444444444444444444
444444444444444444444444444444444444444444444
444444444444444444444444444444444444444444444
444444444444444444444444444444444444444444444
444444444444444444.*
4.

Have a nice day ☺

Your friend,

The Cuatro Killer

A rustling sound came from behind. He had no time to reach for his gun, to turn around. He barely finished reading the letter.

BAM!

Pace hit the ground, the sharp pain in the back of his neck clouding his mind. He could feel the warmth of his blood spread along the side of his neck.

He heard footsteps moving from behind, but the mystery assailant did not move into his line of vision; there was no way he could move his head to get a good look. Even though his mind was foggy from pain, Pace knew his attacker was highly skilled; he was hit in such a way that he became incapacitated.

Suddenly, Pace felt pressure on the back of his neck.

"AAAAAHHHHH!" he screamed. His attacker had pressed their fingers deep inside his wound.

Pace was delirious, groaning in pain. His vision was blurry, but he could see a man's hand write on the ground, using his very own blood as ink. Pace knew the message before his attacker finished: "4."

Pace glared at the number with all the strength he could muster, his vision fading whilst the pain in the back of his neck grew more and more intense. Accepting his fate, he closed his eyes, the intense pain nearly drowning out all his senses. There would be no retirement for him, no final moment of glory for this hardened detective. A feeling of betrayal washed over him, ever so slight; the pain was just too great for deep thoughts. But Pace knew fate was an asshole who just wouldn't let him have a life without the ugly weight of crime hanging over him. The faces of his brethren, the other detectives, flashed before his eyes.

His body would be the next they find.

Finally, in a soft, almost soothing voice, the Cuatro Killer cooed, "And now it's your turn," then the fire of a gun…the last sounds Detective Pace would ever hear.

Cheryl Walsh earned her MFA in creative writing at Virginia Commonwealth University. Her novel *Unequal Temperament* won the Buffalo Books Fiction Prize and is forthcoming from American Buffalo Books in 2023. She has been awarded writing residencies with the Djerassi Resident Artist Program and Brush Creek Foundation for the Arts, and her work has appeared in *Short Édition*, the online journals *Embark* and *Burningword*, the audio magazine *The Drum*, and such print magazines as *Confrontation, Cicada*, and *The MacGuffin*, among others.

Haarlem Proposition

By Cheryl Walsh

Inspired by Frans Hals, Banquet of the Officers of the St. George Civic Guard

She did not want to be here. She had tripped several times while walking in heels along Haarlem's old stone streets, and now at the museum, her ankle throbbed mildly. Her worsted wool suit, dampened by the spring drizzle, clung to her in an uncomfortable imitation of sweat. And the museum's soft light wasn't enough to counter the oppressive darkness of the parqueted walls, but it was too much to permit drowsiness.

Still jet-lagged after three days in the Netherlands, all she had wanted after today's merger talks was to climb the steep steps to her room at the Hotel Carillon and sink into a bubble bath. Maybe have a glass of the local brew—at least she could appreciate the spicy bitterness of that thick Haarlems beer, even if every other aspect of European culture left her American sensibilities unimpressed. But Piet, one of her potential corporate bedfellows, had asked whether she had seen the Halsmuseum yet, and she had been forced to admit she hadn't.

"Julie, you must see it! One cannot visit Haarlem without visiting the Halsmuseum—and it is open late tonight."

Acting appreciative seemed prudent. So here she was, a sophisticated bean-counter terminally unenthusiastic as regards art, surrounded by old paintings of people in strange costumes. Could anyone ever have gone through life in those stiff collars? Not to mention those wide feathered hats that no one but Audrey Hepburn had any right wearing.

She sat down and tried to get interested in the large painting in front of her. It was a group of men who looked vaguely military: swords at hips, furled flags slung over shoulders. Vandyke beards notwithstanding, they reminded her of a bunch of kids who couldn't settle down and pay attention. You'd think Hals would've waited until they were all posed before he started painting.

Then she noticed him. Staring right at her, he tipped his empty glass toward the floor. He was dressed like a clown in a frilly collar, with aqua satin shimmering across his chest. His cheeks were red with drink, and his dark eyes glimmered licentiously. His wet lips parted in supplication: "Fill my cup once more. Or shall I fill yours?"

She felt offended. Sharply offended. Threatened.

Unreasonable, she told herself. She was safe enough. Nearby, a young college-aged couple in tight jeans joked together in French, gesturing lewdly toward a boy with a lute. There were two other men in the room—a middle-aged suit who looked distracted, and an old gray museum attendant who smiled at her.

She turned around on her bench and trained her focus on another group portrait, but she still felt the other's eyes on her. Irritated, she got up and walked slowly, nonchalantly, to the other end of the room and smoothed her mist-dampened hair. She pretended to appreciate the portrait of a stodgy old woman in a white Pilgrim hat, but still, she felt him watching her. She felt his impertinent stare turn to a leer, and she did not like it.

Stealing a glance in his direction, she confirmed her suspicions. His eyes had followed her, and he asked her again to fill his cup, asked again for more than a drink.

Changing tactics, she walked with purpose back to the painting to confront him directly. You're just a painting, she told him silently. Paint. Bits of paint slapped on canvas.

As she leaned in close, expecting him to disintegrate into brush strokes, she smelled the thick Dutch beer on his breath.

His hand touched her breast. She jumped back with a gasp, and he laughed quietly, lasciviously. He touched her again, this time under her skirt, warm moist fingerprints on her bare thigh. She stumbled back with a choked cry, realizing she was naked.

The other people in the room were staring at her. She tried to cover herself with her arms and hands and shouted at the painting, "What did you do with my clothes?"

He laughed and pulled her close, roughly, and the chaotic laughter of his comrades surrounded her. His black mutton-chop sleeve crushed stiffly against the delicate white of her shoulder, and he pressed his wet lips to her breast.

"Fill my cup," he cooed as he tickled her nipples with his Vandyke. "I've filled yours." Then a brimming cup clashed against her teeth, and warm dark beer laced with his breath filled her throat and pushed her into blackness.

"Madam?" A Dutch-accented voice was near.

The floor was hard. The damp wool of her skirt clung to her legs.

She opened her eyes. The museum attendant kneeling beside her blocked her view of the painting.

"How embarrassing!" she moaned.

"Not at all, madam," the attendant said. "It is not unusual."

She sat up and discovered a muted headache. She shook her head. "He attacked me."

"Oh?" The attendant helped her get up off the floor. "So it happens, sometimes." He smiled kindly. "It is a wonderful painting, is it not?" He turned to admire it, but she refused to look at it.

"If, if this . . . happens a lot," she stammered out, "why don't you take it down?"

"It is a great painting!" He frowned in disbelief. "You yourself have felt it."

"Felt it? It felt me!"

The attendant's surprise softened in understanding. "I am sorry it was . . . unpleasant for you." His pale blue eyes were sad. "But we cannot deny others that, how do you say . . . intimate encounter? because yours was . . . unfortunate." He looked back at the painting for a moment, then shook his head. "I am sorry, madam."

And he was sorry. She felt his pity as palpably as the painting's hand, and it quickened her fear as much as her anger. She turned quickly without replying and groped for the exit. As she found the door and her bearings, she clutched her suit jacket closed and escaped into the gray drizzle.

First published in The William and Mary Review (vol. 49), 2011.

Frans Hals, Banquet of the Officers of the St. George Civic Guard – 1627

Anthony Samuels had a late start in writing being an emergency room physician for thirty years in South Florida. He had little time for writing except for patient charting and medical seminars. The author was inspired by the physician and writer, Michael Crichton, and such war novels as *Flags of our Fathers* and *Letters from Iwo Jima*. Dr. Samuels resides in Ft. Lauderdale, with his daughter, where he enjoys reading and writing immensely. His goal is to become published.

Cosmic Showers

By Anthony Samuels

Inspired by an Internet News Article

Key West is the last key in the lengthy chain of islands stretching south from Miami Beach. Noted for being a wide-open town, this five-by-one-mile island, also known as "Margaritaville", is renowned for its drinking establishments, elegant restaurants, carousing, and partying in the streets. It has hosted such legendary writers as Tennessee Williams and Ernest Hemingway. Everything focused on Duval Street in Key West's business district.

Two years ago, the revelers on this street were astonished by a surprise Biblical in its proportions. Around 10:15 PM, a brilliant white light in the skies illuminated the entire key, powerful enough to cast shadows in the night, like a floodlight. What appeared to be an enormous meteorite-like object came streaking through the atmosphere, leaving a lengthy trail of glowing debris. The object crossed the island at a lofty altitude, followed by a powerful, ear-splitting "sonic boom" that shattered the storefront windows at Sloppy Joe's and Captain Tony's. It set off automobile alarms, dogs began to howl, and what few youngsters that were on the street started to cry. Many residents claimed they could perceive the sonic boom vibrate the inside of their chests. Needless to say, 911 was overwhelmed with calls.

The inhabitants thought World War III had begun. Others suspected a UFO or a fighter jet from the nearby Key West Naval Air Station exploded in the night's sky. The entire event lasted a few seconds. Then, the heavenly object appeared to split into four or five brilliant, multicolored pieces that burned up in the atmosphere before they splashed into the Gulf of Mexico's warm waters.

Onlookers ran for shelter inside the many bars and restaurants, fearful for their lives. There was panic in their voices as the astonished crowds commenced to mutter amongst themselves: "Did you just see that? What was that loud explosion?" Several Key Westerners even began praying, "God, save us! It's Armageddon. The End of Days. Repent!"

After things appeared to settle and the streets soon became thick with crowds again, drinking and eating resumed once more, even though many of the inhabitants of Key West remained frightened. At 2:00 AM, the bars closed, and the partiers went home or back to their motels to bed down.

When the natives began to wake up, a bizarre surprise awaited them, as if their island was transformed into an enchanted "Alice in Wonderland" movie scene. Fine, twine-like strands of greenish-yellow, gelatinous goo covered everything like snow. Small filaments, still tumbling from the sky, floated down, akin to feathers from heaven. They ranged in length from several inches to a foot long. Some adhered to each other, resembling a grid – still, others clustered together into marble size clumps.

The material that fell from the sky was on the roadways, sidewalks, tops of vehicles and boats. However, it was not substantial enough to cover objects in a thick layer like a blanket. Much hung from the tree branches similar to Spanish moss. It appeared not to alter shape or melt as the sludge manifested a faint, eerie, florescent glow. The inhabitants came out to sweep the streets and walkways, brushing filaments off automobiles and plucking them from the trees. Most of the Jell-O-like goo was placed into large piles curbside to be taken up by the sanitation trucks, like piles of rubbish from another Fantasy Fest, a Halloween festival comparable to New Orleans' Mardi Gras.

Rumors started to circulate around town that the strands and clusters of the gelatinous material were causing the town's people to become sick.

The ailment was found in individuals who had more than a casual contact with the substance. Those afflicted picked the strands up with their uncovered hands to make snowballs and frolic in it, animated by never seeing snow in Key West before. Many developed severe migraine-like headaches requiring medical therapy. The substance overcame others with vertigo, nausea, and vomiting, similar to seasickness. Affected individuals said this was the worst illness they had ever had. Many dogs and cats became ill. Several of the smaller ones died after becoming listless and anorexic, even after ingesting minimal jelly-like material.

One fateful story was of a Key West police officer starting rounds early in the morning. Officer Robinson sat in his patrol car and ran the windshield wipers to clear away the mysterious substance from the glass. Instead, it smeared the material over the windshield, obstructing his vision. Not wearing gloves, the officer took several rags out of his vehicle. These rags, along with windshield washer fluid that the patrolman squirted onto the glass, helped him to take most of the material off, enough so he could see. Later the unfortunate officer was discovered slumped over the steering wheel of his police cruiser at a red light near the center of town. The officer was unconscious, with froth and saliva drooling from his mouth.

Another tragic event was an aged mother living alone in a trailer who was discovered by her grandson on the kitchen floor, retching and gagging, too weak to support herself. She was sprawled out in her own emesis for the prior two days, so sick the elderly woman could not move her head without becoming ill. EMS rushed the woman to the ER for treatment, where she required hospital admission for intractable vomiting.

It was said a group of rowdy teenagers were playing catch with an egg size, balled-up cluster of strands. One of the adolescents dared another to eat a teaspoon size quantity which resulted in the youth promptly vomiting and then having a convulsion lasting several minutes. The others became dizzy and nauseous and scattered home to their parents. Other individuals had to leave work early or cancel their vacation plans altogether.

Many Key Westerners began gossiping amongst each other. Most felt the noxious substance was a military biological weapon dispersed among the people in a top-secret experiment. Just days before the event and on the morning of the "cosmic shower", several black ops helicopters and jet airplanes from Key West Naval Air Station were observed. After the toxic goo stopped falling from the sky, three Humvees, colored black with no markings visible, were detected on the roadways. Each had two soldiers in hazmat suits picking up, bagging, and labeling samples for analysis. The military has been known to experiment on their own soldiers. Recall the dawn of the nuclear age and the Cold War when tests about radiation exposure, mind control, and LSD were run by the CIA on the military and even civilians. What a better location than an island for a closed, controlled environment, like a gigantic petri dish for the armed services to carry out their experiments on humans. The Navy quarantined the entire island with roadblocks, and the harbor was closed to boat traffic. Local officials, putting on heavy gloves and facemasks, began scoping up samples to be transported to the astrobiology lab at the University of Miami.

After several days of investigation by experts at this institution, the scientists prepared a written statement for the local Key West authorities. The astrobiologists claimed they remained baffled about the peculiar substance that fell from the sky like snow and sickened many individuals. Under the microscope, they could establish the strands of green goo were comprised of microscopic lattices. A transparent, protective gelatinous material covered the bizarre substance, similar to that found occurring over amphibian eggs. It was determined the greenish-yellow substance resembled a material designed for the military to transport agents such as noxious chemicals or pathogens to populate future battlefields with virulent organisms and poisons.

Mysteriously, these particular lattices were bare. If they were carrying something, the substance must have been delivered into the environment beforehand.

It is unknown if the toxic goo came from a meteorite, our military, or if they deemed the sludge to be extraterrestrial. What lingered on the pavement, trees, and on rooftops turned a faint brown color, withered, and either blew away or dispersed into the surroundings.

Later in the day, a local newscast stated another meteor landed in Tampa Bay the night before, causing quite a scare amongst the local residents. Will they also experience a comic shower similar to the "Star Jelly" shower of Key West?

Khadijah Danielian is a writer and artist from New Jersey. She graduated from The New School with an MFA in creative writing, and was a long time member of the JC Slam spoken work poetry community. When not reading novels and fanfiction, she is busy writing her own stories.

Fireside

By Khadijah Danielian
Critical Role, Campaign Two

The Mighty Nein had taken shelter from the storm in a nearby cave on the path to their next destination. They'd finally disembarked from their ship about a week ago and had begun the trek to Eiselcross. Fortunately, Caleb's locator spell had come through for them just before the worst of the snowstorm hit. They could dig or magic their way out tomorrow when the storm ended, even if the cave entrance got snowed, but for now, they would rest.

Dagen had chosen to make his little corner of camp farther into the cave, and the hardened dwarf ranger was snoring away in his wheelchair, flecks of drool freezing in his beard. Still close enough to the Nein if there was any unexpected danger, but not enough to seem part of the group.

If he hadn't spent so much energy earlier that day, Caleb would've happily brought them into his Nascent Nein-Sided Tower, where they'd be warmer and safer. As it was, he didn't even have much energy for the dome, not that there was space for it in this cave anyway. Caleb pushed down the guilt, recognizing that they were all exhausted.

At least they were together and safe, for now.

Everyone except for Caleb was asleep around the low-burning fire they'd made. Beau's head was cradled in the lap of a lightly snoring Yasha. Fjord, arms crossed and snoring, was slumped against the wall. Veth was using his thigh as a pillow, and Caduceus had just come off watch duty. Jester was huddled by the half-orc with her back turned to Caleb because, of course, she'd feel safest near Fjord. As she should.

Frumpkin was curled in his lap, and the wizard stroked his familiar's soft fur as he watched the flames dance. Even if he hadn't been on watch, he couldn't have slept.

He knew by now he was a glutton for self-flagellation. After telling everything to the rest of the Mighty Nein and his dinner with Ikithon, he was slowly coming to recognize that, yes, he'd been manipulated in his youth.

But that didn't absolve him of his sins.

That didn't make the nightmares and memories disappear. They didn't consume his dreams as often these days. Sometimes, he could actually get a good night's sleep, but other nights like this one...well, he wouldn't let himself forget. Couldn't. To forget would mean risking the same mistakes again, and he would not be the death of another family.

Caleb sighed a bone-deep sigh and pulled his blanket and scarf 'round himself tighter. He twitched at the sounds of someone stirring from inside the cave. They should have been the only ones there. It was only Jester, though, and he relaxed.

The little blue tiefling sat up, rubbing the sleep from her eyes. He couldn't tell if she noticed him, but Jester scooted closer to the fire regardless. Caleb's heart warmed at the way the near smoldering flames painted her blue skin in a golden hue, how they reflected in her purple eyes like dancing lights. She truly was...enchanting.

But then he noticed she was shivering. Surely not from the cold, what with her being resistant to it and all. Upon closer scrutiny, he saw a thoughtful sadness in her eyes. No sign of her usual easy cheer or mischievous glint.

A sad Jester was not allowed in his books.

Caleb gentled the orange cat out of his lap and onto Veth's. Then he stood up and softly padded closer to Jester by the fireside.

"Couldn't sleep?" Caleb asked in a whisper, carefully moving to sit next to her.

Jester jumped a bit but smiled when she saw it was only him. "I could ask you the same thing, y'know."

"I've got watch duty," he said, shrugging. "Besides, I…"

"…Bad dreams again?" Jester asked with genuine concern. Caleb nodded. He sometimes forgot she was more perceptive than she let on. "I'm sorry you have to deal with that. You don't deserve it, Caleb."

Don't I? "I'm used to it."

They sat in silence. He didn't want to push just yet.

After a few moments, Jester spoke.

"Pretty cold up here, huh?"

"*Ja*, very bitter. Though I suppose you're more comfortable than the rest of us."

"Yeah, but even for me, it's pretty chilly."

"Mm. You are looking a tinge more blue than usual."

"Feeling a bit more blue too…."

Caleb looked at her, brows creased. "Well, uh, perhaps you could paint a dick on Dagen's face while he's sleeping." They looked over to the dwarven ranger. His nose popped a bubble before he grumblingly cozied further into his chair, unconsciously clutching his ax. "I wouldn't have the balls—which are a bit frozen right now—but I won't stop you."

She seemed to think about it for a moment but then half shrugged in her expensive coat. "Eh. Better not. Don't want to make him mad."

Jester's face showed only half the mirth she'd normally have at the prospect of dick graffiti. The tricksy cleric hadn't even giggled at his ball joke. *Not a good sign.*

"*Ja*, you're right. Best to keep our guide dick free."

The fire crackled. The wind howled outside, and a bitter breeze ghosted through the cave. After a few minutes of not quite awkward but not quite comfortable silence, Caleb wondered if Jester might have fallen asleep.

"Do…" Jester looked up at him, a worried crease on her brow. "Do you think it was a mistake? Taking this job with Vess DeRogna. Coming up so far north?"

Caleb blew heat into his hands. "It's what we all agreed upon at the time. True, we're getting a lot more than we bargained for, but we were bound to come up this way anyway because of Moll—of the Nonagon. Especially after what happened with Vess DeRogna."

"Yeah... that's true."

"...Is that what's keeping you up?"

"I was just...thinking. About home. About the Traveler. About who *I* am because of him… and not. …I keep thinking about Molly. Or, I guess, *not* Molly? And what we're going to do once we're back in the Empire, *if* we get back to the Empire, and all of Beau's theories and—" Jester sighed. "I dunno. It's a lot."

Caleb hummed in agreement. He knew how hard this new unknown factor of their (former?) friend was on all of them. With Jester, it must've been particularly difficult. Of course, Yasha had it the worst, having known Mollymauk the longest out of them. But Caleb knew how much the young cleric treasured her friends, and she hadn't even been able to really say goodbye. Despite the optimistic mask she wore around the others, Caleb knew how much that truly ate at her.

"Do you think we might die up here?" Jester whispered so softly Caleb almost missed it.

He turned to her fully, concern written all over his tired face. He tried to think of the right response. He wasn't good at pretty lies or hopeful encouragement. She was too smart for that anyway. So he took a breath and carefully formed what he hoped was an honest yet gentle response.

"I... hope that none of us will," he said, keeping his voice soft. "There is always the possibility of danger, but that's nothing new to us."

"I know. And we're all pretty powerful, but... It's so easy for people to, like, freeze up here or fall off an icy cliff or get eaten by weird monsters or something, and I just—" Jester took a shuddered breath and wiped at the corner of her eye. Caleb could just make out the scraggly crimson fur of Sprinkle within Jester's hood, nuzzling his owner in his sleep. She gently petted his soft head. "What if I never see Mama again? Or what if one of us, or all of us— I was alone for a really, *really* long time. I almost lost my best friend at Rumble Cusp, and I...I don't want to lose any more people that I love."

A snowy gust crept into the cave, and Jester shivered, pulling her travel-worn cloak around her uselessly. Her tail wrapped around her as she pulled in her knees. It pained Caleb to see the woman he lo— cared for worrying herself to this level of turmoil. Caleb scooted an inch closer. He was no good at words. He was better with actions and gifts, with magic. That was his love language. So, he dug down for whatever scant bit of energy he had left and—even though it was probably a bad idea to be wasting his magic on something like this because they might run into trouble and need spells, but it's Jester, so it was worth it—cast dancing lights.

As always, Jester's eyes sparkled with wonderment at the amber lights. Her natural smile started coming through, and Caleb's heart fluttered.

"I am tired as hell right now, yet I can still find it in me to cast a spell or two," he said. "So if I can do this now when we are safe for the time being, I think I and everyone else here can find a way to keep fighting. To keep each other safe if something were to happen." He let the spell dissipate and turned his full focus to Jester. He almost couldn't bear the way she looked back at him. So full of faith in his words and power. "We've gotten pretty good by now at getting out of bad scrapes, *ja*? Also, we have Caduceus, and we have you. Plus, we've got Dagen on our side, and he's managed to survive this place."

"That's true," said Jester.

"And we have the temples you and Caduceus made as backups. True, teleporting is tricky and risky here, but it's still a last resort option."

"Also true."

"But... if things got really bad, I would do whatever it takes to make sure you get back home—that all of us do. I..." Caleb clenched and unclenched his hands. He pictured them turning ashy black and cracking with heat. "I don't want to lose another family either."

Jester stared at him, and Caleb had to fight the urge to look away despite the ever-reddening blush on his face. *Well, at least my nose isn't cold anymore.* After a few seconds, though, Jester hummed thoughtfully and smiled at him. For real, this time.

"Thank you, Caleb. That makes me feel a lot better." If he didn't know any better, he'd swear she was blushing. *Wishful thinking, Widogast. Probably just the firelight.*

"Ah," Caleb cleared his throat. "You're welcome. Of course. Anytime. Now, you should probably get some sleep. I believe Yasha and Beau have the next watch."

"Y'know, I might be able to sleep easier if I was warmer. Maaaaybe you could lend me some of your body heat?" she asked, scooting even closer to him.

Caleb's face was crimson. His brain short-circuited for a second. "I–I uuuuhhh."

"Not like that, silly." Jester teased. The fact that she was messing with him was definitely a sign she felt better. "I mean like cuddling up for warmth."

"I thought you, uh, had resistance. To the cold, I mean."

"Well yeah, but it's still pretty cold even for me. Soooo?"

Embarrassed though he was, Caleb couldn't help but chuckle. She had that effect on him. He hesitated for only a second, then wrapped his arm and the blanket around Jester. She quickly melted into his body.

"Are you warm enough?" Caleb teased.

Jester's giggle melted into a cozy hum. "Much better. Thank you, Caleb."

"Of course. Can't have you catching a cold," he smirked.

"Because I'm our second-best cleric, right?" Jester asked, already dozing off.

"Because you're you," he said seriously. "And you are...wonderful."

She hummed sleepily. "You're pretty wonderful too."

Jester turned her head to give him a gentle, almost shy kiss. She missed his cheek, and her lips landed on his neck. It was the softest of touches, yet the spot of his skin felt like it was burning. Caleb couldn't help holding her a little closer, a little tighter. He even felt so emboldened as to reach up and brush his gloved fingers over her freckled cheek, his touch feather-light. Afraid to burn her like he'd done everything else good in his life in the past. He couldn't help himself from wanting to protect her from everything else in this world, if not from himself. She was more than capable of protecting herself, but he wanted to support her all the same, to make sure she never felt alone again.

Caleb knew all about fires. Both their blessing and their curse. He understood fire as intimately as his real name, and Jester... her fire was like a hearth. Warm and glowing golden. He felt it when they first danced, over time as they got closer, and even after he read to her the beloved children's book he'd shared with his mother, the last tie to one of his happier memories from the past. The Nein had come to feel like a new family to Caleb, but Jester felt like...home.

It was dangerous to feel this way. Useless. Yet, despite himself...

"Jester?"

"Hmm?"

Caleb sighed and said in perfect Zemnian, practically choking on the heart in his throat, "*Ich habe mich in dich verliebt.*"

Jester nuzzled closer into him. He could tell from the slow rise and fall of her chest that she was already asleep. She most likely hadn't heard a word he said, even if he'd used Common. It's better this way. The wizard whispered goodnight to his cleric with a light peck on the top of her head between the horns.

Caleb looked around at the cave filled with his friends (and Dagen), then back down at Jester. A soft smile rested on the corners of her lips. Even the firelight seemed at peace. He smiled and allowed himself to relax and drift into sleep.

This was enough for him. The Mighty Nein had taken shelter from the storm in a nearby cave on the path to their next destination. They'd finally disembarked from their ship about a week ago and had begun the trek to Eiselcross. Fortunately, Caleb's locator spell had come through for them just before the worst of the snow hit. They could dig or magic their way out tomorrow when the storm ended, even if the cave entrance got snowed, but for now, they would rest.

This was enough for him.

MEMOIRS

Dan R. Tardona was born and raised in Brooklyn, New York. He recently retired from the National Park Service where he served as a Biologist/Park Ranger for 32 years. In retirement, Dan lives in Jacksonville, Florida with his cat Shilo. Dan enjoys writing nature poetry, short stories, and is working on his first novel when he is not serving with the U. S Coast Guard Auxiliary as a Marine Safety and Environmental Protection Staff Officer.

Stirred by Seafaring Art and Poetry in Brooklyn

By Dan Tardona

Inspired by Rime of the Ancient Mariner

As I climbed the steel steps up to the second landing of the Brooklyn Library to the Literature section, I came across a book cover that caught my eye. Being a rather young reader at the time, the art depicted on book covers was intriguing to me, and that was how I picked books to read. Needless to say, I was quite fond of illustrated books. The cover showed a striking faded blue drawing of a man with outstretched arms. His hands were clutching onto shrouds of a sailing ship, and he was standing at the top of the mainmast high above the deck while the ship was being tossed about in the middle of a raging sea. At that moment, I did not know what those ship parts were called, but the entire image just fascinated and excited me. Then I read the title which intrigued me even more, "Rime of the Ancient Mariner" by Samuel Taylor Coleridge and illustrated by Gustav Dore. It was this writing and illustrations that began my lifelong journey of learning about the sea, poetry, and nature in general. In many ways, it influenced my choices as to where I wanted to live and work. I have only recognized this recently. But back to that fateful day in Brooklyn.

I was not sure what a mariner was. I was pleasantly surprised when I took the book off of the shelf and drifted through the illustrations depicting all kinds of seafaring marvels.

Each new picture filled me with a sense of adventure, danger, mystery, and anticipation.   At that point in my life, I did not have any sense of poetry or understand what poetry was all about. I started to read the words that had such wondrous sounds to me despite the fact that I did not know their meaning at that moment in time.

Understand that I was very young and living in a poor neighborhood of Brooklyn, New York, with very little, if any, exposure to the sea. I had never seen the ocean. I was at first only captivated by the illustrations and great-sounding words. I had no clue as to what the words meant, but I loved saying them to myself "mariner," "albatross," "skiff," "gale," and what the heck was a "lighthouse?"

After checking the book out, I ran all 6 city blocks to our flat above the Puerto Rican grocery store, up the stoop and 16 steps to the apartment door, rushed in, and spewed out a barrage of questions about the book. My mother was always happy to stop whatever she was doing to explain things to me and slow me down when I was so excited. She had a way of encouraging my excitement but somehow calming me down at the same time. She saw the book in my arms and asked me to it to show her. Smiling, she began to tell me that I had picked out a wonderful book and suggested we look at it together. Mom was a very well-read woman despite the fact that she was a high school dropout (though, later in her life managed to get a college degree). Before she started to read to me, she asked me what it was about the book that made me so excited to read it. I told her about the pictures in the book and the words I had never heard before. She explained that it was good that I noticed the words and went on to tell me about poetry and the way words are sometimes put together to express feelings and ideas in an artful way. She told me how the sounds of the words, along with their meaning, were like the art of the pictures in the book that I liked so much. I think it was at that moment that, for the first time in my life, I began to appreciate art and the many forms that art can take.

Inspired

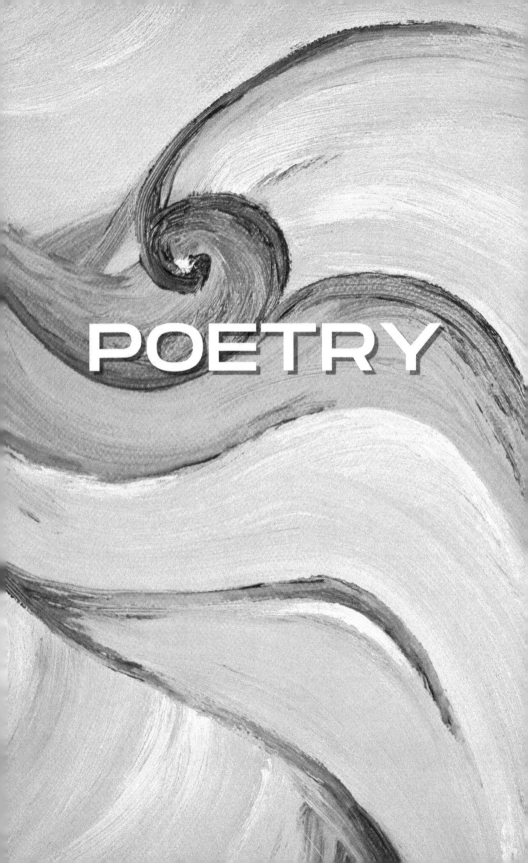

T.C. Anderson is a Houston-based writer and artist with work published in *Sunday Mornings at the River, Capsule Stories, Pages Penned in Pandemic: A Collective, The Raven Review,* and more. Her poetry collection, *The Forest,* published in 2021, serves as the inspirational basis of an art installation with artist Mari Omori premiering in 2022. Her artistic and collaborative work has been shown in several local art galleries, as well as online and internationally. A graphic design professional, Anderson holds a B.A. in Graphic Design & Media Arts from Southern New Hampshire University.

Space Cowboy

Inspired by: Jeff "Joker" Moreau from the Mass Effect series

You say you can make this girl dance,

but I really want to know if you can make her ride,

for a true space cowboy doesn't need a lasso

to help his woman see the stars,

only a smooth grip on her hips and

a sweet whisper in her ear.

You say you can unshackle these chains,

but I really want to know if you can break these barriers,

for a true space cowboy doesn't see walls

but mysteries that

only his experienced hands and

cool lips can solve.

You say you can rock my world,

but I really want to know if you can wear this vessel thin,

for a true space cowboy doesn't see a body

but a history to learn, and

only he has the keen eye and

practiced patience to learn it.

You say you can make me see nebulas,

but I really want to know if you can make me feel them,

for any pilot can ride galaxies,

but a true space cowboy makes his ship

breathless.

A Promise Kept to a People Who Forgot What It Felt Like to Fly

Inspired by Jeff "Joker" Moreau from the Mass Effect series

You tell them I'm in good hands, and I'll even be home before the night kisses the moon, and I hope it isn't true, because I want to completely lose myself in you, lay forever buried beneath your skin, and never see the rotation of the sun.

I want to feel you like no other has as we dance amidst the stars together, your hands stroking Saturn's rings around my belly, your tongue Mars's heat against my flesh, your fingertips tracing Neptune's chill down my spine, your eyes glowing asteroids carving new destinations into my untouched surface.

They would call it hormones or a phase or a crush, but no, they don't understand my need for you at the helm, steering me, guiding me, moving me, tempting me slowly, desperately, ravenously, explosively, softly, repeatedly, over and over and over and over again as we create a new night sky with the nebulae we splash recklessly against the dark, a night where time never ends and a curfew doesn't exist, but we do.

The clock strikes ten and I'm at my door on your arm like the gentleman you are, a promise kept to a people who forgot what it felt like to fly.

You leave me with the stars we birthed anew in my glowing, overcast eyes and promises of another new night.

Stephanie Lamb, founder, and EIC of Quillkeepers Press, LLC, earned her Bachelor's in Business Accounting and later switched gears to further her education in Creative Writing. She has had a lifelong love of literature, which led her to study classic and contemporary writing forms. Lamb has had a passion for writing since she was a teenager when she wrote to process her feelings, triumphs, and traumas in a healthy manner. She went through almost a decade-long writer's block in her mid-20's when she sought medical intervention for insomnia and chronic anxiety. Now, she writes to purge negative feeling, so she doesn't become them, and also for her own healing. She shares her work publicly, hoping it helps heal others.

Lamb is also the author of *Verbal Vomit and Other Poetry and Prose,* which is available on Amazon. Although we hear it is in the process of being revamped, and the original version won't be available much longer. Additionally, she has been published in multiple journals, anthologies, magazines, as well as online publications by various presses.

Portia's Gold

Inspired by Shakespeare's "The Merchant of Venice"

They say eyes are the window to the soul and mine have many lifetime's worth of stories to tell. Between the pause of each beat lie silent parables of love's martyrs birthed and abandoned, dreamed and forgotten. Hearts inflated with the breath of the cosmos that wrap around the pulse of gypsy comets oscillating like plasmic tidal waves in my arteries. Silver seafoam floods beckoning for a sliver of salvation. But the soul knows what it needs, like a spring sapling with outstretched arms through the permafrost begging the sun to deliver it to better soil. And I am no different. I am all tender leaves, binding roots, and a desire to return to forgiving skies. But I am grateful for unanswered prayers and undeveloped wings, because as Portia's suitors learned *'all that glitters is not gold'*.

Previously published in Verbal Vomit and Other Poetry and Prose

Winter is Coming

Inspired by Game of Thrones

The winter arrived too soon, and swords sprung from our tongues and we were cloaked in nothing but twilight and blood. *There was so much blood.* And you drew a line in the proverbial sand, and I flew a white flag, and we collapsed gasping and grasping at the tempest brewing in each other's throats. Clawing and gnawing its way to the surface to expose the eons of truths left unsaid. Truths that held no salvation. Truths tossed and scattered like the stars that spangled the sky to hold the heavens in place. And I stood stripped and trembling, asking for one last truth. *When did the sun begin to loathe the moon?*

Previously published in Verbal Vomit and Other Poetry and Prose,   and Honeyfire Lit Mag - Memory Foam

Tin Man

The tin man did not have a heart

So he exclaimed I would be perfect to play the part

I fell for his lies and empty pseudo love

Not realizing the depths of his desperation

I was hellbent to find a heart in his rusted-out chest

Maybe it is just camouflage and blending in with the rest?

I cracked his ribcage and dissected the mess

Finding nothing but a stone tucked away under his breast

A rotted-out chamber where a heart was supposed to be

Blinded by love, I just could not see

What I did next, I barely lived to regret

I thought he could have mine as if it is something you could sublet

Shoving my fist down my own throat

I ripped out my heart and the blood pooled like a moat

I presented the treasure to the tin man

and he smiled as he licked the blood from my hand

As the color drained from my face

my body went flaccid

I could tell this time the container had corroded the acid

He did not show the least bit of shock nor surprise

while my heaven and hell rose to collide

It was as if he had traveled that yellow brick road before

Sickened, I realized he was immune to the gore

The tin man did not have a heart,

So innately I suppose none of this is his fault

I can only blame myself for such a callous assault

He left me in the fields for the ravens to pick apart

Whispering…

'Pick her pretty bones clean

I'm going to need them for my art'

Previously published in Verbal Vomit and Other Poetry and Prose

Superman

It will be months before our paths cross again. Your hair will have grown longer with the scent of a new lover tangled in its locks. And my heart will have eclipsed the moon with desperate wonder. Wondering if you are thinking of me, and has the other side of the bed gone cold, are you sleeping well, or... not at all? Do you still drink your coffee as black as the crows cawing songs of promise on the dawn of a new day? I wonder how much of me you still carry with you like a cameo locket noose taut around your neck? But I lost count of how many times we've said goodbye, only to stumble our way back to each other again with our hearts in our careless palms and dignity caught in our throats. But I can't deny all roads have always led back to you. And you in jeans and a worn tee will always be my kryptonite. And I, Lois Lane, will always be posted on the ledge, preparing for the next freefall.

Mark Andrew Heathcote is adult learning difficulties support worker, he has 200-plus poems published in journals, magazines, and anthologies both online and in print, he resides in the UK, from Manchester, Mark is the author of "In Perpetuity" and "Back on Earth" two books of poems published by Creative Talents Unleashed.

Almond Blossoms the Deferring Sentence

Inspired by Van Gogh's "Almond Blossoms"

Some early gnostic paraded his knowledge

weren't they a bunch of unbearable, know it all's

with fraternities and with rationale

they'd have harden-up-insides icy, soon as blossomed.

Van Gogh saw the blossoming springs; the Almond

as-a-special tree to him, it was part of the chancel

that represented a pearl of hope amidst a backdrop of darkness

But here are some know-it-all atheists seen laughing at him

his eyes and veins were swollen full to their bursting brim.

God doesn't-exist forget your brushes, your oils, your gospels

those apostles, don't sing that nonsense hymn,

don't paint those blossoms;

you're all just deferring your sin.

Orlando

Inspired by Virginia Woolf's "Orlando"

This portrait picture of Orlando
is still somehow strikingly fresh,
her lineaments dress no scarecrow.
Whether it's male or female
a heavy-suit is a father's crèche
a caring parent makes us wear
myself I wore genderless clothes
when able to pay for my wares.
It's as striking as eyes set on a raven
still to see a woman like Vita,
wearing her Sunday best.
Her manly appearance aroused both sexes
her face, quite oval, her jawline pronounced
she was a poet of changing seasons
a poet of fluctuating genders
Sissinghurst Castle Garden,
was her one and only, blank white canvas?

The Artist's Restorative

Inspired by Pablo Amaringo

The visions of Pablo Amaringo

transport us to magical wonderlands

it's like oil & water had amazing-

hypnotic properties and-I-expands.

Ayahuasca art resonates with me.

But it's short-lived, too hectic for my pleasure.

Like some hallucinogenic sari,

the "real beauty lies" within its nectar.

That went about healing the painter's soul.

For me, there is a stiller-reflection

in those water lilies - powers - enthral.

Monet canvases each flower-a-brethren.

Each blue eggshell brush-stroke heals like a balm;

such are the properties of great artists.

That they can find within to such aplomb,

a composure arriving, some solace-

they've got this almost restorative knack-

of lifting our tired, beleaguered spirits

the poet, speaking tongues elegiac;

doesn't he do the same - sweet and viscous?

Inspired

Dana Trick, born a first-generation Mexican-Canadian-American autistic with ADHD, lives in Southern California where it is clearly foolish to wear black any day but she does it anyway. Besides writing, she spends/wastes her day by either reading weird books and comics; researching the history of certain topics because she is an historian and has the degree to prove it; drawing crappy art and comics strips; and/or watching an unhealthy amount of cartoons, anime, and YouTube videos. Her work has been published online—in the *Art of Autism*, the *Lothlorien Poetry Journal, The Quiver Review*, and *The Ugly Writers*—as well as in print with the *Moorpark College Print Review* and the *Realm Of Emotions* anthology. She wishes the reader a nice day.

A Poem About Guts from Berserk

Inspired by Kentaro Muira

He is too terrifying and too violent

To be a hero in a fantasy manga;

He can only be a monster.

He is too spiteful and wrathful

To be a man burdened his scars and trauma;

He can only be a force of pure rage.

He is too fragile and too lonely

To be a strong man that wields a sharpened slab of iron as a sword;

He is more of a stifled wail of pure despair.

He wants to be happy too much

To be an anti-hero character in a senien manga;

He can only be human.

Utena

Inspired by Be-Papas

Ever since you crawled out of that coffin,

You were always in revolution.

Sword in your hand,

Rose upon your heart,

You strode with nobility and strength

As you fought against the decorative cages that princes and princess

Bury themselves in.

You swore

That you'll never be weak, that you'll protect the weak,

That you'll never lose your nobility and kindness,

Like the prince you adored—

Then you fell in love with a rose that could only grow thorns

And obeyed the demands of a man who pretends to be a prince.

You tried to save her as a prince that you thought you were,

But when it mattered the most to you and her,

She and you received thorns that tore each of you apart.

That's when you cried revolution,

Prying open the fairytale coffin of pain with your tears

And held out your trembling hand to your rose, your love, Anthy,

Swearing that you'll never lose her again.

And ever since then,

You never let go of her hand.

Anthy

Inspired by *Neil Gaiman*

You gave the world your roses,

And they gave you thorns,

Too many thorns, so many thorns

That you started to grow thorns instead of roses.

You know what happens to princes—

You got the trauma to prove it,

The burden of the witch who "stole" the world's light.

You had to endure those swords of hate for the sake of your prince

Because you loved him too much to realize

His fairytale was an illusion that only brought an eternal apocalypse

Where the stars no longer shine and miracles only bring misery.

However,

One day,

A girl with rosy hair, wearing a prince's clothes,

Blooming in revolution,

Pried open your coffin cage,

Hand outstretched,

Screaming definitely,

That you are not a witch, not a bride, not a princess—

But that you are Anthy,

Who lives freely like the beautiful roses.

And ever since then,

You never let go of her hand.

Button-Eye Witch

Inspired by Irrational Games

Beware the Button-Eye Witch of the secret door,

For she will steal everything you ever held precious—

And eat your soul.

If tangled within her horrid web

Of your own sweet dreams and wonderous wishes,

Make your heart brave and sharpen your mind with cleverness.

Trick her into a game of hide-&-sneak

Where you'll scratch out her eyes

And drown her hand into the forever-well,

Set free the stolen souls and trapped eyes.

Would You Kindly . . .

Inspired by 2K Australia

Would you kindly

Despise this parasite's poem

That accused our objectivism's utopia

Of dystopian hypocrisy?

Would you kindly

Harvest this inhuman girl

To heighten your chance of survival,

To maximize the profits of selfishness,

To continue the Great Chain's corruption?

Would you kindly

Fly frantically towards

The paradise's dwindling flames

In tune with the sad mad march hare's dance?

Would you kindly

Devour all the vicious sinner-eves from the abandoned,
98

Devour all the vile adams' apples from the rotting

In this garden of capitalist evolution?

Would you kindly

Continue digging tombs for the silent forsaken

As they all drown in rapture?

Inspired

Enoch Black is a mythopoet. He writes on myriad themes, but more times than not there is a red thread back to mythology or folklore, either ancient or modern. He's waiting impatiently to become a dragon of deep midnight purple and lavender flames. In the meantime, he's going to continue to write poetry and fiction. You can keep up with Enoch on his website:

www.stormdragonbooks.com

Why I Love Dragons

Inspired by Dragons

Flying fiercely or floating far afield,

Wings are their only refuge, their sole bield.

Freedom is their friend, solitude their shroud,

Soaring draped in a bond of wind and cloud.

Wandering to the edges of the earth,

Sleeping where they please, all the world their berth.

Wild as the trees, fiercer than lightning storms,

Oft they shift and shape taking many forms.

Their power is like shuddering thunder,

Yet they are like children filled with wonder.

All life and nature are beauty to them,

Each experience, a sparkling gem.

Embracing the deep fire of their core,

They light up the night with that fury roar.

They love when they will without an excuse,

They reject others' anger and abuse.

You ask me why I love dragons so much?

Simple, they bring me magic, just a touch.

Sleeping Dragon

Inspired by Dragons

Let sleeping dragons lie.

If you want to live, you'll comply.

That's not who I am though.

Pushing my limits is how I grow.

So, pour me another flagon.

I'll tell you an epic story of a sleeping dragon.

Dragon Songs

Inspired by Dragons

Dragon fire sings

songs of mighty gliding wings

and of wyrmkin kings

Roaring battle cries

smoldering and fearsome eyes

terrors of the skies

Adventure calls them

wanderlust their dearest gem

fiery diadem

Grandeur is their name

majesty is their great fame

beauty is their flame

Onward through the moonlit night

Now they serve as stars so bright

What Is a Group of Dragons Called?

I would love to live with a clowder of cats,

But I also think it would be neat to fly among a cloud of bats.

Dark would be my sins if I were to hobnob with a murder of crows,

But not nearly as dark as it would be with a pack of wolves and all their woes.

An unkindness of ravens I would seek,

But a thunder of dragons would really release my inner geek.

Bruce Parker holds an MA in Secondary Education from the University of New Mexico. His work appears in *Triggerfish Critical Review, Pif, Blue Unicorn, Cerasus,* and elsewhere. He lives in Portland, Oregon, and is an Associate Editor at *Boulevard*. He has published a chapbook, *Ramadan in Summer*, (Finishing Line Press, 2022).

The Hunt

Inspired by Pieter Bruegel the Elder (1525-30-1569) Hunters in the Snow (1565)

I turn my back on my dead

like a hunter in the snow

whose weapon has misfired.

I press on through the cold woods,

seeking the tracks of the hart

which has wounded me.

I am old as a Flemish painting,

varnish cracked and yellow,

a saint whose suffering

means nothing. To suffer

is only to keep walking in the snow,

to make the line of footprints

longer than necessary.

Hunters in the Snow by Pieter Bruegel Elder

Aleatoric Ode to Alexander Liberman (1912 - 1999)

Inspired by Alexander Liberman

The element of chance in

all things can be

represented by poker

chips tossed on a

canvas followed by careful

application

of paint. Ideas dropped in

the mind, words brushed

on or a random sentence

the mould into

which ideas then poured are

sometimes the key

to the question what is art.

MB And then the random throw came into your process of painting.
AL I had always been involved in chance. I read the *I Ching*. The whole idea of the throw.
Gravitation played a role, attraction of systems. I was involved with a very intense order
of life.
MB How did you create chance?
AL I bought poker chips of two colors—one set was all black and then I just threw them.
I put tracing paper over it and traced and then filled it in with color.

—- "Alexander Liberman," interview by Marshall Blonsky
bombmagazine.org/article/774/alexander-liberman accessed Sept. 14, 2015

Inspired

James Abbott McNeill Whistler (1834 - 1902),

Lady Mieux (1881)

Inspired by James Abbott McNeill Whistler, Lady Mieux

The artist draws my eye down

along the gown of Lady Mieux,

down her arm, doubtless downy,

through swirls of fabric to the floor.

I adore Lady Mieux, not for her flowing

flowery waterfall of skillful paint,

it is her face which holds me,

her look that stops me at her door

unable to leave her until she

unwithholds her permission

who is like a persimmon that will not yield

to a lover's bite, lest there be more.

William Merritt Chase (1849-1916)
Did You Speak to Me?, about 1897

Inspired by William Merritt Chase, Did You Speak to Me?

She turns to every viewer who walks up in the hope that

someone has noticed her studying the pictures now behind her,

has asked which she likes or why her father left the unfinished one there,

or had he ever imagined the onlooker might be

one hundred eighteen years away. She was so engaged

in looking that she was only aware someone spoke,

addressed her perhaps, but she did not hear the words distinctly.

Her question lingers, and though I have not spoken all morning

I stammer in my mind, *why, yes, I asked which picture you like the best*

as she looks up at me. When I have moved on

she will turn back to look at the pictures and ponder my question,

but when another onlooker approaches,

she will turn again and ask in the same plaintive voice,

Did you speak to me?

oil on canvas, .91 x 1.04 m (36 x 41 in.)
The Butler Institute of American Art, Youngstown, Ohio

Gelatin Print on Paper

Inspired by William Merritt Chase

They stand four in a row, from right
Mortimer Menpes, William Merritt Chase, Whistler, unidentified man,
surely an artist like the others though he lacks the gleam
of Whistler's monocle,
their top hats like the funnels of a steamship.
They haven't the smiles of modern folk, no need to bare
their teeth for the camera, insouciant enough
in their pose, all but Whistler expecting rain
with umbrellas to hand;

      but James Abbott McNeil Whistler deftly holds a slender cane.

           It is 1885.

Whistler called Chase "Colonel" for reasons not given
          or no reason at all.

        Chase sat for him
which he found fatiguing:
        Whistler would not allow him to move,
        screamed at him to stay still;

the sittings went on for days, weeks.

The two finest artists of their time
agreed to exchange portraits.
        Chase caught Whistler's persona
        and his tonal harmony technique
        and his attitude
so accurately, in what was almost a caricature,
        that Whistler denounced his portrait bitterly
and the friendship ended. Perhaps Whistler wished
he had painted it. "You will, James," Chase might have said,
        "You will."

          It was 1885,

for them it was *now,* the artists lived in their own present,
did not know what the next moment might bring
    (did not dwell
    in dread of it)
went through their present as if drawn by a string

   dwelled in comfort
   able man's world
   highly skilled
   hard working
   at play, at ease.

     Who took their picture?

Relax, let's eat some chops and drink
some good wine
   (let's top
   each other's
   wit).

The gelatin print in the archive in Water Mill, New York, is
black and white, stop-motion:

   they were breathing,
   the trees were green,
   they turned to one another,
   they walked down the street,

the photographer went to his studio,
printed the photograph and we still see it
every day if we want to.

     It is not 1885.

The four artists captured

     (let us call
    the unidentified man
     an artist)

are dead.

We have the works of their hands,
the etchings and illustrations of Menpes,
Whistler's mother (*Arrangement in Grey and Black No. 1*),
more than five hundred paintings done by Chase
in various media,
idle hours,
children at play,
fish, sand hills, sea grass, scrub,
accomplished young women,
paintings that, like their subjects, glow, tell stories, disclose firm character,

try all ways.

    We still have them
    on walls in galleries, museums, homes:
they belong
to our now, to someone's tomorrow.

Inspired

Roger Camp lives in Seal Beach, CA where he muses over his orchids, walks the pier, plays blues piano, and spends afternoons reading under an Angel's Trumpet with a charm of hummingbirds. When he's not at home, he's photographing in the Old World. His work has appeared in Poetry East, Rust+Moth, Gulf Coast, Southern Poetry Review and Nimrod.

The Cisco Kid

Inspired by The Cisco Kid

was a friend of mine,

the first on the block

in black and white

our Philco gathering

the neighborhood at night.

Riding horses in the San Gabriel

a dry riverbed

studded with stunted willows

and mined with rusty cans

the petite, pig-tailed blond

not deigning me a glance

always got the white stallion

cantering ahead of the pack.

Astride the brown

surrounded by my posse

real and imagined

riding the paint and palomino

Diablo and Loco

every Saturday

we rode her down

and into the sunset.

Art History's Splashy Smear

Inspired by Self Portrait by Van Gogh

Van Gogh's *Self-Portrait with Bandaged Ear*
supports the received story
of the sliced lobe
wrapped in a soiled sock
and gifted to his favorite whore,
the tale of the crazed artist
art historians love to paint.

The revisionist version
restores Gauguin
to his rightful place
in the canon of infamy
having grazed Vincent's ear
with his foil, a deft feint
to defend himself
from a madman.

Still, museums continue to spin
their cavalier smear,
their insatiable appetite for color
over bare-backed, black and white facts.

published *Last Stanza Poetry Review*

Kimberly McAfee is a writer and poet residing in the US. She has authored/co-authored works in a variety of formats, such as websites, e-magazines, anthologies, and even a peer-reviewed scholarly journal. Ms. McAfee has also self-published three chapbooks available on Amazon. She is currently working on her first full-length poetry collection. You can find more of her poetry on her Instagram page @writerpoetkim.

Sorry, Sorry: Forever Love

Inspired by "Sorry, Sorry" by Super Junior

Sorry, Sorry

This heart will only love you

From now until forever

It is you I belong to

Sorry, Sorry

If you want my love to grow dim

It roars strong and bright

An ocean of feelings within

Sorry, Sorry

Even if we ever part

You have enchanted me

It is you who has my heart

Sorry, Sorry

For talking this way

I want you to know I love you

I want you to know that I will always stay

The Silver Smartphone

Inspired by "The Red Wheelbarrow" by William Carlos Williams

"so much depends upon"

a silver smartphone

fully charged

"beside the" pile of white paper bills

Inspired

Karin Eaton is a writer, traveller, and student of Ancient Egypt. After retirement, she moved with her partner from Toronto, Canada to the rural tranquility of Lake Scugog, Ontario, where she enjoys the challenge of experimenting with memoir, travel, and writing poetry. She has had poetry published in two *Mythos Poetry Society Journals* and *The Legion, Branch 270 Seniors Literary Anthology 2020-2021*. Her travel memoir, *Conversations with Elephants* was published in the Quillkeepers Press *Botany of Gaia* anthology.

Into The Abyss

Inspired by Gwendolyn MacEwen

Out of confusion comes a light

further on the road ahead

than I had thought to travel.

A guiding light, or a warning

sight of you inspires me

to venture on the untrodden path.

Ahead, the black abyss beckons

with uncertain promise.

My body, willing to accede, stops,

distorts, teeters on the brink

Held back by doubting mind,

resisting the awful unknown.

Fear and bias tear the joy apart

if truth could be obscured.

But your ray still shines

across the deep abyss.

And knowing you have travelled there,

I will surely follow.

A Humble Salute to Amanda Gorman

Inspired by Amanda Gorman at Joe Biden's Inaguaration

I have seen the face of hope

and heard words that sing of truth

filling the gaping hole deep within the soul.

Ushering in a time to reflect,

to heal and move the rhetoric.

From her heart to yours,

wisdom beyond her years.

Follow the trajectory of the rising star

from gloom to glory

from despair to hope.

Watch while the impossible is dissolved

See how everything suddenly becomes possible.

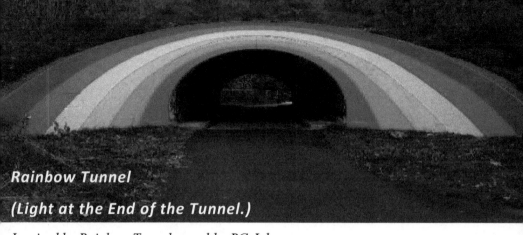

Rainbow Tunnel
(Light at the End of the Tunnel.)

Inspired by Rainbow Tunnel mural by BC Johnson

What mysteries does the rainbow hide?

What stories does it share?

What happens if you go inside

for those who travel there?

A portal to epic fantasies

born of love, crafted with great care

this rainbow has rich memories.

A memorial to one who died.

a message of hope and caring.

And when you step inside

there's space for dreams and sharing

amidst stories painted bright.

And if you venture further,

the tunnel leads you to the light.

Reflections On a Wall

Inspired by a mural painted by John Hood

A thousand words or more are penned

beneath the coloured coats of ever marching men.

The shades of horse and soldiers tell stories of the past.

while brushed reflected light mirrors moments of today.

The wall, once grey and silent, drums now with vibrant life.

Destiny summoned closer by steady beating feet.

The hopes and dreams and sorrows of long forgotten men

Are captured here forever in a tapestry of time.

Inspired

Daniel Moreschi is a poet from Neath, South Wales, UK. After life was turned upside down by his ongoing battle with severe M.E., he rediscovered his passion for poetry that had been dormant since his teenage years. Writing has served as a distraction from his struggles ever since. Daniel has been acclaimed by numerous poetry competitions, including The Oliver Goldsmith Literature Festival, the Westmoreland Arts & Heritage Festival, the Utah State Poetry Society's Annual Contest, the Deane Wagner Poetry Contest, Jurica-Suchy Nature Museum's Nature Poetry Contest, and the Hugo Dock Snow Maze Poetry Contest. Daniel has also had poetry published by The Society of Classical Poets, and The Black Cat Poetry Press.

Solar Swansong

Inspired by Twilight Mount Desert Island, Maine by Frederic Edwin Church

When terra's tilt instills our skyward views,

The depths of lazuline begin to wear

A sudden nascency of subtle hues

That run as traces of a golden glare.

This fusion blurs and burns horizon lines

While pliant seas reflect a lasting haze:

A flight of fluid flames that intertwines

With clustered clouds that now seem set ablaze.

A veil prevails, with flickering reach, yet leaks

A burgeoning, blackened blend it can't contain,

That spreads a speckled reach along the peaks

And trickles down akin to ashen rain.

A touch of twilight soothes the fervent zest

Of blood-like remnants duly laid to rest.

T.M. Thomson's work has been featured in several journals, most recently in Soundings East. Three of her poems have been nominated for Pushcart Awards. She has co-authored *Frame and Mount the Sky* (2017) and is the author of *Strum and Lull* (2019) and *The Profusion* (2019). Her full-length collection, *Plunge*, will be published in 2022.

Fig Mother

Inspired by "Fig Mother" by Leonora Carrington & "The Flautist" Remedios Varo

Fig Mother feeds many—squirrels, mockingbirds,

honeybees, woodpeckers, possums, crows, a gaze

of raccoons, night after night, leather paws pulling,

twisting, blade fangs taking the lead on chewing

& flashing at the passing shadows of the human

animal with spindly limbs, daytime eyes & upright

malice.

Fig Mother bears the imprint of snake & blood.

Sun (sus)stains her, moon cools her, July ripens her.

Fig Mother is a flautist—she plays August, filling

mouths with sweetness, toughening bone, easing belly.

Poco a poco she tickles the spine of summer, hangs

like purple notes on trees with leaf-hands, opens red

& pulpy, smudging lips, teeth, bills, paws, mandibles,

ground with a maroon crescendo as plump as midnight

moon.

Rumors of Spring

Inspired by "Rumors of Spring" by Aaron Laidig

It thrums in thunder's crack & purr

rolling around basin of hill & hollow

It rides rain to ground in a gully washer

slipping from cloud & ending in petrichor

It glints in sun on a cool day, eluding

capture but spangling grass with orange

It whelms with the incense of soil freed

from ice & flowing with crocus roots

It rattles air with crystal wings of bumble bee

as she shivers snapdragons into pollen surge

It creeps with fox over field & through woods, seeking

the small & succulent & cherries beetling from branches

Inspired

It spirals with ribbon snake around log & stone & drowses

at river's cusp, biding March's alloy of frost & fever until witch hazel

throws off snow, stretches & shimmies its saffron fingers in April's air,

lilac-blazed & coiling around my body, widening my eyes

to receive a sky swelling with storm & sun

& unfolding with trillium's

bright trinity.

Reflection

Inspired by "2000 Light Years" by Peter Max

Give your reflection a try:

it will rise out of swamp/ocean/

lake/creek/estuary/delta/puddle—

a delight from foothill to peak

your hoary mountain of a head

will give way to mossy tress

& oak nose & moon eyes

overseeing it all.

The you you perceive is backed

by stars & earthworms & skulks

of foxes/wisdoms of wombats/

a richness of martens/an ambush

of tigers & O So Much More.

Sing your reflection(s) into ripples.

The list of all you lust for comes fast:

speed of wind/rage of storm/weight

of monsoon/sheen of dew & weight-

lessness of cloud-wisp & grass blade

& Then Some.

They will tell you you can't have it

Any of It but you flow with floe

gush with gully washer that you

bestow—a jubilee of splash

& leaf & lane/an artery

of rain & pebble/elixir

of fertile loam

& rising mist

a song of shimmer.

Grazing

Inspired by "Sister of the Moon, Fantasia" by Leonora Carrington

Play that violin as your lovely light skin

echoes the alabaster sky shedding its rain.

The waterfall of your dark dress narrows,

slips through a winged belt—a bat pointing

downwards, alighting on your hips, crashing

to earth, impossible to tell which, impossible

moods, impossible you.

Fay surround you—limping imps, pixies

with pomegranate wings, sylphs slick

with silt from slothful rivers, goblins

robed in spiderwebs, gremlins flashing

sharp teeth. All throw parrot flowers

& monkey orchids at your feet, shod

with puddle-blue boots.

Let the storm rage, I tell you, overhead

with cloud & growl & lightning cracking sky

open like an opulent egg, & in this breast

of swirling fog & sepulchral tones & ragged

lame horse rhythms—it watches through my eyes,

moon-saucers, loves your spin, arpeggio, drift

of elbow, drone, cadenza.

I kiss your wings into being, vertebra by vertebra,

until they thrash & vibrate a blue that rivals lapis

lazuli & kingfisher & chicory & racer snake

& elderberry & Neptune & sea holly. And now

you waft over smoke trees & jewel millets

that reach for you with downy fingers

while my fingers graze

on hair as pearled with clouds as the molting sky.

Maria Sibylla Merian,

17th Century Artist & Naturalist, as Goddess

Inspired by the art of Thomas Woodruff

In my mind you stroll

under cloud-shrouded moon

a book & watercolor brush

in hand   wherever your soles

touch soil roots snake out—

earthy wakes behind you.

You wear a train of conks

brown & brittle & teeming

at its ends with butterfly & moth—

a dazzling folly writhing

with petal wings—velvet blue/

milk spotted/faun brown/stained

glass/never ceasing/never alone

with thick-rinded oranges for suns

& red pepper clouds & violets

on stems like waves

& whitecap leaves. Nothing

is ever still. Even the spider web

off in the distance sings like a harp

when small winged bodies

touch it or when you draw it

squirming with life

with death   a context you weave

from cathedral fig & orchid

bullet ant & lantern fly

grass & caterpillar

starry-eyed.

Phyllis Castelli returned to her North Carolina hometown after a career in music. She delights in time spent with her lifetime special interests: writing, music, photography, a pollinator garden, and black Labrador Retrievers. Phyllis is interested in creating projects that knit together the beauty of all those favorites.

Peace

Inspired by "The Adoration of the Shepherds" by Antonio da Correggio

Following the star,
I gentle wrap my heavy heart
and lay it in the manger.

In the stable bare,
I let myself in gladness weep.

While ox and lamb
do steady gaze,
I lay to rest my weary head.
Safe in that moment's simple grace,
I sleep.

Through still night,
the snow falls clean,
a blanket bright and dancing white.

I am new.

Suzanne Cottrell lives with her husband in rural Piedmont North Carolina. She's an outdoor enthusiast and retired teacher, who enjoys reading, writing, knitting, hiking, Pilates, and yoga. She loves and is an advocate for nature. Her poetry has appeared in numerous online and print journals and anthologies. She's the author of three poetry chapbooks: *Gifts of the Seasons, Autumn and Winter; Gifts of the Seasons, Spring and Summer;* and *Scarred Resilience* (Kelsay Books). www.suzanneswords.com

What's the Rush?

Inspired by "What's the Rush?" painting by Jenny McKinnon Wright

eyes set on autumn coastal skies
darkened by swirls of feathers
black skimmers swerve in unison

perform a percussive composition
synchronized beating wings
churrs of kak-kak-kak

sea birds search for herring
their lower black and orange bills
rake through shallow waters

feeling fish, mandibles snap shut
I hunger for a pat on the back
for a job well done, my steps quicken

I plow through life, my thoughts migrate
should I change jobs, seek a friendlier
environment? birds migrate

to warmer climates, food sources,
breed, for protection of marshes,
estuaries while I sequester

within an office cubicle
from administrative pressures
conferences of yak-yak-yak

why do I want to fly up
the corporate ladder, work long hours,
travel, miss my family

black skimmers in flight
what appears chaotic
is orderly and purposeful

I will focus and set
forth a clear direction
After all, what's the rush?

Inspired

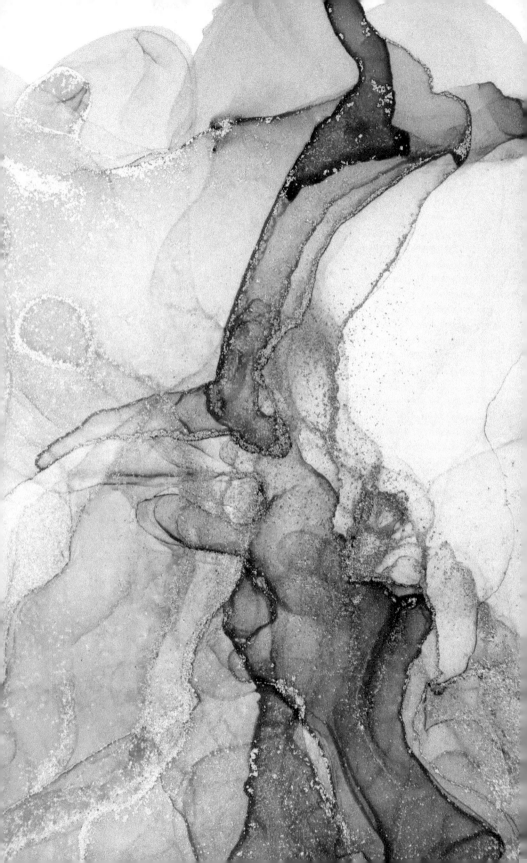

Jenny McKinnon Wright is an award-winning artist who believes that working in plein air allows her to "capture the emotion that only painting in that location can offer."

For those who have her work, Wright's sense of color shines through. Although she is personally enlivened by the locations she paints, those places can become the viewer's own experience. Wright's paintings can be seen in Sunset River Marketplace Gallery in Calabash, NC, in select locations in the region, and in private collections.

"Something captures my eye---the light, the lines, the colors that I actually see. If the light on an old building is glowing in the late afternoon, I might underpaint the scene in a warm red. Later, that underpainting will shine through and give the painting the glow that captured me earlier."

A plein air painter who works primarily in oil, Wright's formal art training began at East Carolina University in Greenville, North Carolina, and continued with graduate work in Atlanta at Georgia State University. She has taught art in the North Carolina and Georgia school systems and instructs private students. Inspired as a student by the Impressionists, Wright continues to study with recognized plein air painters.

What's the Rush?
ry, McKinnon Wright

Inspired

About Us

Quillkeepers Press, LLC is a small indie press and indie author resource group. We publish themed anthologies on a variety of topics, as well as provide resources and services to indie authors. We pride ourselves on reasonably priced services that include book cover design, book cover formatting, interior design, interior formatting, marketing design, publishing consulting, and an array of editing services. It is a deep passion of ours to help as many writer's voices be heard as possible. As indie artists ourselves we understand most creatives operate within a strict budget. Therefore, it has always been a priority of ours to keep our rates reasonable. Our corporate climate is not one of profit but one of helping bring dreams to fruition. Our motto sums it up best "Reading between the lines, to make your words take flight".

We produce between 3 and 6 anthologies annually. We never charge for artists to be published in our anthologies, although a small reader fee may be associated with our ad space on submittable.com to cover the cost of the ad space, ISBN number registration, copyright fees, as well as other overhead costs. As writers ourselves, we understand how hard the market can be. How challenging it becomes to get work into the hands of a larger audience. Therefore, we accept and encourage our contributors to submit both new and previously published compositions (as long as the previous publisher allows it). Too often, we find publishers who want exclusive rights to the work being published. This is counterproductive if the artist wants their message to be received by as many people as possible. Having been in and studied the industry for years, our founder has concluded that many writers take great pride in their work and produce it for their own healing. Furthermore, they share said work hoping it helps others heal.

For all the aforementioned reasons, it is our current policy to ask for non-exclusive rights to our contributors' work versus exclusive rights. In essence, our artists are allowing us to borrow their prized writing, and we are incredibly grateful.

It is also for those same reasons we consider ourselves an indie publishing services company, rather than a traditional publisher.

Traditional publishing usually requires an extensive contract and exclusive rights to work and royalties. We rather help wrap artist's products into a beautiful package and allow them to set their own parameters, price points, and keep all their royalties from sales.

On a final note, whether you have employed our services or lent us your voice in an anthology, thank you for entrusting us with your craft. If you would like to participate in a forthcoming anthology, please check out our Submittable page at www.submittable.com . For more information on our services, please visit our website www.quillkeeperspress.com

Keep the quill moving,

Stephanie Lamb, Founder, EIC

Quillkeepers Press, LLC

Other Books Produced by Quillkeepers Press, LLC

Soon, A New Day
A rise of the Phoenix themed anthology of essays, memoirs, short stories, and poetry by various artist

Turning Dark into Light and Other Magic Tricks of the Mind
A mental health themed anthology of essays, memoirs, short stories, and poetry by various artists

Rearing in the Rearview
A parenting themed anthology of essays, memoirs, short stories, and poetry by various artists

Verbal Vomit and Other Poetry and Prose
A poetry and prose collection by Stephanie Lamb

Tan Lines
A Summer Solstice inspired anthology of memoirs, short stories, and poetry by various artists.

Bare Bones
A Halloween inspired anthology of essays, memoirs, short stories, and poetry by various artists.

Snowdrifts
A Winter Solstice inspired anthology of essays, memoirs, short stories, and poetry by various artists.

Sapling
A Spring equinox inspired anthology of essays, memoirs, short stories, and poetry by various artists.

Dislocated
The debut poetry collection by Dylan Webster

Botany of Gaia

A nature inspired anthology of essay, memoirs, short stories, and poetry by various artists.

Harvest

A Fall equinox inspired anthology of essays, memoirs, short stories, and poetry by various artists

The Matador's Wife

A chapbook length collection of poetry by Andrés Colón.

scars & lyres

A chapbook length collection of poetry by ww harris

Lightning Source UK Ltd.
Milton Keynes UK
UKHW022222211222
414209UK00008B/45